# THE INGLIS LECTURE
## 1958

# THE INGLIS LECTURES

## THE INGLIS AND BURTON LECTURES

An Emerging Program of
Secondary School Mathematics

# An Emerging Program of Secondary School Mathematics

MAX BEBERMAN

HARVARD UNIVERSITY PRESS

CAMBRIDGE, MASSACHUSETTS

1962

DISTRIBUTED IN GREAT BRITAIN BY
OXFORD UNIVERSITY PRESS
LONDON

LIBRARY OF CONGRESS CATALOG NUMBER 58-12962
PRINTED IN THE UNITED STATES OF AMERICA

## THE INGLIS LECTURESHIP

*To honor the memory of Alexander Inglis, 1879–1924, his friends and colleagues gave to the Graduate School of Education, Harvard University, a fund for the maintenance of a Lectureship in Secondary Education. To the study of problems in this field Professor Inglis devoted his professional career, leaving as a precious heritage to his co-workers the example of his industry, intellectual integrity, human sympathy, and social vision. It is the purpose of the Lectureship to perpetuate the spirit of his labors and contribute to the solution of problems in the field of his interest. The lectures on this foundation are published annually by the School.*

# An Emerging Program of
# Secondary School Mathematics

# An Emerging Program of
# Secondary School Mathematics

## INTRODUCTION

IN 1952, a few of us at the University of Illinois asked ourselves: Can able mathematicians together with skillful teachers develop materials of instruction and train high school teachers in their use so that the products of the program are enthusiastic students who understand mathematics? An affirmative answer could be justified only by a constructive existence proof, and we set ourselves the task of furnishing such a proof.

We are still at work on this task. The core of the working staff consists of Herbert E. Vaughan of the Department of Mathematics of the University of Illinois, and Gertrude Hendrix, William T. Hale, Eleanor McCoy, and myself of University High School, the laboratory school of the College of Education.[1] A group called the University

[1] Others who, in earlier years, made substantial contributions to the development of instructional materials are G. P. Hochschild, B. E. Meserve, and D. A. Page.

1

of Illinois Committee on School Mathematics (UICSM) serves as an advisory board to the staff, and draws its membership from the Colleges of Education, Engineering, and Liberal Arts and Sciences. I serve as administrative head of the project; Hale and I teach some of the newly developed courses at the laboratory school; Vaughan provides the principal mathematical substance of the program; Vaughan and I write the instructional materials, with considerable assistance from the other members of the staff; and Hendrix and McCoy direct the teacher-training phase of the project.

We now have courses for the four high school grades on trial in classrooms in a dozen pilot schools. Some forty teachers and over seventeen hundred students are participating. Some of these students are gifted eighth graders (or highly gifted seventh graders); the rest are students who would ordinarily be enrolled in conventional "college preparatory" or "academic" mathematics courses.

Our courses are still in the process of development. Portions of them have been used for as many as three consecutive years, but other portions are very recent revisions or are entirely new. One result of this experimentation and revision is our recognition of two major principles which we have used as guides in developing courses and in teaching students. For a time, these principles operated at a nonverbal level. It is only recently that we have been able to verbalize them and to identify them as our basic guides. A major portion of this report is devoted to the presentation and illustration of these principles.

The development of a new course of study is not undertaken in a vacuum. One has in mind an image of a student and a catalog of the student's knowledge and misknowledge. A student entering the ninth grade knows something about arithmetic and geometry; he has available to him a battery of algorisms for computing with "unsigned" real numbers, he is aware of some arithmetic generalizations, he has learned quite a few mensuration formulas, and he has solved many "practical" problems which involve applications of arithmetic and geometry. The curriculum developer also has in mind the traditional expectations of what a college-bound high school graduate should know of mathematics. He is expected, among other things, to solve equations (singly and in systems), to use algorisms and formulas in transforming algebraic and trigonometric expressions, to deduce theorems from postulates, to find ordered pairs which belong to relations, to graph relations, and to apply his knowledge to a host of geometric and physical problems.

We think that these objectives are sensible and proper, and our curriculum is planned accordingly.

But we insist upon an important qualification: the student must *understand* his mathematics. Now, the word 'understand' and its close relative 'meaningful' have been bandied about in educational circles to a point where just about everyone pledges allegiance to the goal of teaching meaningful and understandable mathematics.[2] We have tried to translate these words into operational terms. We believe that a student will come to understand mathematics when his textbook and teacher use unambiguous language and when he is enabled to discover generalizations by himself. These two desiderata — discovery, and precision in language — are closely connected, for new discoveries are easier to make once previous discoveries are crystallized in precise descriptions (it is easier to discover how to solve equations when you know what an equation and a variable are!), and skill in the precise use of language enables a student to give clear expression to his discoveries. Despite the tie between these two facets of understanding, I shall, for convenience' sake, discuss them separately.

PRECISION OF LANGUAGE

The procedure through which a child becomes

---

[2] Although mathematics educators now seem to regard 'meaningful mathematics' as platitudinous, it is greeted with warmth and surprise by most laymen. This lay attitude is surely an indictment of the conventional program.

aware of a mathematical entity such as a number or a function is undoubtedly quite complicated and has yet to be described. However, let us assume that there are such things as mathematical entities, that their existence is nonphysical, and that human beings do develop awarenesses of them. As a child becomes aware of such an entity, he may want to talk about it. In such a case, he needs a name for it. Consider the preschool child who notices that to dress her three dolls she must have three dresses, three hats, three parasols, and three pairs of shoes. Her awareness of the *class* of sets of three things is an awareness of an entity. The entity is the number three and a name of the entity is the word 'three'. But the existence of the entity does not depend upon the invention of the word 'three', and the fact that a child may be acquainted with the word 'three' cannot be considered a sure sign that he has even the slightest awareness of the number three. To say that a child understands the number three is to say that the child is aware of this class of matching sets. He demonstrates this awareness by asserting correctly (through action or through words) that a given set either belongs or does not belong to this class. If the child is to function as a social being, he needs to communicate his awareness and, therefore, he needs a name (a word, perhaps merely a gesture) to denote the mathematical entity.

The social intercourse which is facilitated by the invention of a name undoubtedly results in a sharpening of the awareness and, therefore, in a "deepening of the understanding" of the entity. But an increasing familiarity with a name should not invest it with the properties of that which it denotes. The name and entity are distinct and must not be confused. It is our contention that in the exposition of elementary and secondary mathematics there is so much confusion of names with their referents that in many cases the student has never discovered that there is a distinction between symbols and their referents. Confusion in exposition is of little consequence to a student who has managed to maintain for himself the distinction between mathematical entities and the symbols which denote them because most of the time, as the cliché goes, "the intention is clear from the context". But, for the student who has not yet become aware of the mathematical entities in question, an exposition which is guilty of this confusion is just about useless. It is even dangerous, for a student can through imitation give behavioral evidence of understanding even though the awareness which is part of understanding is missing. Let us consider some illustrations.

On several occasions I have given to seventh-grade classes the following problem:

Find a number which when added to 7 gives 7 as the result.

(This problem followed several others of a similar type: Find a number which when multiplied by 3 gives 27 as the result, or: I am thinking of a number. If I divide it by 4, I get 6. What number was I thinking of?) In some cases, when a student said that 0 was the number in question, another student protested that 0 was not a number but that it was, instead, a place holder. Here, in rather bold terms, is an example of the danger arising from a confusion of the number 0 with the digit '0'. Even though every digit is a place holder in the decimal system of numeration, it is most unlikely that a student would protest, for example, that the number 6 is a place holder rather than a number. He has an awareness of the entity 6, and does not confuse it with any of its names even though one of its names is used as a digit. It is likely that the student learned that the symbol '0' was used as a mark in constructing numerals before he had become aware of the entity 0.[3]

Certain remarks made by junior high school students lead me to suspect that they believe that, among the rational numbers, there are pairs of rationals which can be added and that there are pairs of rationals which cannot be added. For

[3] It has been suggested that many of the so-called "zero difficulties" experienced by children in carrying out the multiplication and division algorisms can be attributed, at least in part, to the confusion between '0' and 0. In this connection see Robert S. Fouch, "The Un-sanity of Mathematics and Its Teaching,"*ETC.* (Winter 1954), pp. 113–121.

example, they may say that "you can add 2/7 and 3/7 but you can't add 2/3 and 1/2". When a student asserts that the sum of 2/7 and 3/7 is 5/7 and that the sum of 2/3 and 1/2 is 7/6, he must mean that he has added rational numbers in each case. But he also recognizes that the simple algorism illustrated by:

$$\frac{2}{7} + \frac{3}{7} = \frac{2+3}{7} = \frac{5}{7}$$

cannot be applied to the expression:

$$\frac{2}{3} + \frac{1}{2}.$$

In fact, he may even assert that he must first "change the numbers" before he can add. This colloquialism is harmless if he recognizes that '2/3' and '4/6' are names for the same number, and that '1/2' and '3/6' are names for the same number, and that when he writes '4/6 + 3/6' instead of '2/3 + 1/2' he is referring to the same sum by using a new expression which is more convenient because it can be simplified by the algorism illustrated above. But if he regards 4/6 as a different entity from 2/3 because '4/6' is different from '2/3', he does not understand the rational number 2/3; and perfect scores on tests which measure skill in adding rational numbers are not evidence of such understanding. (A similar example of the confusion of symbol with referent is the case of the senior high school student who stoutly maintains that you can add $2\sqrt{2}$ and $5\sqrt{2}$

and get an "exact" answer but that you can't expect to get an exact answer when you add $2\sqrt{2}$ and $5\sqrt{3}$.)

Another illustration in support of our contention that comprehension can be blocked by a confusion of numerals with numbers is to be found in reactions to textbook treatments of "number systems with bases other than 10". Many students show considerable surprise and wonderment when they learn that they can do the same things with base-two "numbers" as they can with base-ten "numbers". The very use of the word 'number' in the description of this subject is misleading because what is under discussion is the construction of numeral systems, that is, *naming* systems. In textbooks one can read statements that there are binary numbers, trinary numbers, quinary numbers, octic numbers, decimal numbers, and duodecimal numbers, and that the *same numbers* in these different systems are *different* — for example, 31 in the quinary system is different from 31 in the decimal system. A revealing test of the understanding of someone who claims to understand "change of number base" is to ask (using conventional language) the following question:

Take the prime number 13 in the decimal system. In the octic system this is the number 15. Is it also a prime number in the octic system?

Any hesitation at all in giving an answer to this

question is a sign that the answerer's understanding is not all it should be. Of course, if the question is posed in language which shows a recognition of the distinction between number and numeral, the "problem" vanishes:

Take the prime number whose decimal name is '13' and whose octic name is '15'. Is it a prime number?

As soon as one recognizes that primeness is a property of numbers, he also recognizes that it is not affected by changing the name of the number in question.

I have come upon an able student who thought that numbers in the binary system are bigger than in the decimal. This assertion is excusable if you are willing to believe that he meant numerals when he used 'numbers'. But, what about the student who maintained that there were *more* integers in the binary system than in the decimal system? It is hard to fathom the nature of this student's awareness of integers.

If the mathematics teacher's (and the textbook author's) sole job in the classroom were to furnish the student an example of someone in the act of "doing mathematics", there would be little need for worrying about the distinction between symbol and referent. And, it must be admitted, many students do learn mathematics by regarding teachers and authors in just such a light. The first actions of such students are imitative; the brightest ones among them eventually puzzle out meanings by themselves. However, we believe that teaching should be more than just something which enables students to learn to use symbols by imitation. Teachers and authors should deal directly with the problem of teaching students how to use symbols, and the procedure for doing so requires only that the expositor use an unambiguous mode of expression. If one is to write a description of how to use symbols, one must, when doing this, mention or refer to symbols. But in mentioning symbols one must use names for them. For example, in the sentence:

   '6363' contains '63' twice, but 6363 contains 63 one hundred one times,

the first clause refers to symbols, and the second clause refers to numbers. The symbols "6363" and "63" are names for the numerals '6363' and '63', respectively, while the numerals '6363' and '63' are names for the numbers 6363 and 63, respectively. Undoubtedly, a reasonably intelligent person could divine the author's intention if he wrote:

   6363 contains 63 twice, but 6363 contains 63 one hundred one times,

but the simple act of inserting single quotation marks to form names of symbols makes the meaning clear and immediate. Other examples of sentences involving both the use and the mention of symbols are:

(1) '31425' has 5 digits and denotes a number which is divisible by 5;
(2) '3 + 4', '8 − 1', and '7' are names of 3 + 4;
(3) '2/3' and '4/6' are different symbols, but 2/3 is 4/6;
(4) 'the principal square root of 2' is a description of $\sqrt{2}$.

In the instructional materials which have been developed by the UICSM staff, careful attention is paid to the problem of distinguishing between the use and the mention of symbols. We feel that this distinction helps us to say precisely what we mean in those cases where a direct statement is useful. (There are cases where important notions can be communicated readily by example and in which the only value of a direct statement is that it provides the writer with an interesting exercise in rhetoric. The algorism for multiplying a whole number by 10 is such a case: the product of a whole number by 10 is the number named by adjoining a '0' at the right-hand end of the decimal numeral of the given number.) A student who has only a tentative feeling for the referents of the symbols used or mentioned in a statement is in a poor position to guess "from the context" the writer's intention. It is in such cases that precision of statement is an almost necessary condition for understanding.

Another compelling reason for distinguishing, both in written exposition and in teaching, between symbol and referent is that it prepares the student for a consistent and simple explanation of the use of letters in mathematical expressions. Here is an area of mathematical instruction that is fraught with linguistic difficulties. A student who has been deluded into thinking that a numeral is a number can be floored when he reads that a letter is a number also. (And the notion that a letter is a "changing number" must be surprising indeed!) A student who reads in a conventional textbook that a letter is a symbol for a number must experience a certain amount of uneasiness when he tries to understand explanations of the use of letters in sentences such as:

$x + 3 = 5, x + 4 = 10$, and: $x^2 + 1 = 17$.

In the first sentence he learns that '$x$' stands for 2, in the second that '$x$' stands for 6, and in the third, as a capstone to this silliness, that '$x$' stands for both 4 and $-4$. By the time he encounters a sentence such as '$3 + \sqrt{x} = \sqrt{(5 - x)}$', where he is told that '$x$' stands for no number at all, he may not be overly disturbed because he has given up trying to find a consistent explanation of the use of this peculiar symbol.

He may also be told in a conventional course that he can add $3x$ and $5x$ but not $3x$ and $5y$, although multiplication does not seem to be so selective.

He has learned that he can tell that $-2$ is a

negative number by observing the minus sign in '−2', but he has also learned that he is wrong if he uses the same criterion in deciding that −*x* is a negative number.

He knows that when he multiplies or divides both sides of an equation by the same "quantity" there is some danger of altering the set of roots if he is not careful about excepting 0. But, since he feels free about adding the same quantity to both sides of an equation, he may experience some consternation when he compares the set of roots of:

$$3x + 5 - \frac{1}{x-2} = 11 - \frac{1}{x-2}$$

with the set of roots of:

$$3x + 5 = 11.$$

In his geometry course he may learn:

Axiom 5. A quantity may be substituted for its equal,

and then wonder what is wrong with the following demonstration:

| | Given: *AB* is parallel to *CD*. To prove: ∠ *y* and ∠ *z* are vertical angles. |
|---|---|
| 1) *AB* ∥ *CD*. | 1) Given. |
| 2) ∠ *x* = ∠ *y*. | 2) Alt. int. ∡ are = |
| 3) ∠ *x* and ∠ *z* are vert. ∡ | 3) Def. of vert. ∡. |
| 4) ∠ *y* and ∠ *z* are vert. ∡. | 4) Ax. 5.          Q. E. D. |

This catalog of oddities can be extended and elaborated.[4] However, I think that I have made the point that conventional exposition concerning letters in mathematical expressions is confused to such a degree as necessarily to confuse a student.

How does the UICSM handle the problem of explaining the use of letters? In the first place, our students are aware of the distinction between numerals and numbers. Although our ninth graders may not be able to *say* what numbers *are*, they are aware that numbers have existences apart from their numerals, and that a mark on paper such as a '5' is not the number 5. They know, also, that each number has many numerals, that a sentence formed by connecting two numerals by an '=' is an equation, that such an equation is a true sentence if the numerals connected by the '=' are names of the same number, and is a false sentence if the two numerals are names for different numbers. A sample of the exercises which lead up to a consistent explanation of the use of letters is to convert:

$$\underline{\hspace{2cm}} + 5 = 9$$

into a true sentence by writing a numeral in the blank space, and to convert it into a false sentence by again writing a numeral in the blank space. We vary the appearance of these sentences-to-be-

[4] See Karl Menger, *The Basic Concepts of Mathematics* (Chicago: The Bookstore, Illinois Institute of Technology, 1957).

completed by using other marks besides blanks; for example:

$$\square + 3 = 8, \ 2 + \triangle = 1, \ 15 = 4 + \diamondsuit.$$

These expressions which contain '='s, and blanks or frames are also called 'sentences' or 'equations' because they have the same form as sentences and equations. But the student quickly discerns the difference between, say: $\square + 3 = 8$,

and: $7 + 3 = 8$, or: $5 + 3 = 8$.

In the second and third cases we have sentences which are either true or false, while in the first case we have a sentence which is neither true nor false. (Although '8' is a numeral, '$\square + 3$' is not. So, the '=' in '$\square + 3 = 8$' connects neither numerals for the same number nor numerals for different numbers.)

The student notes that a sentence such as:

He is the author of David Copperfield

is like the sentence:

$$\square + 5 = 13$$

in that each is neither true nor false and each can be converted into a sentence which is either true or false by replacing the 'He' or the '$\square$' by a name. The marks 'He' and '$\square$' are pronouns, marks which hold places for names. Students are easily led to invent the word *pronumeral* to designate the class of pronouns which hold places for numerals. The transition from frames as pronumerals to letters as pronumerals is readily accomplished — it is easier to write letters than to draw frames. But the important notion is well established: pronumerals are not numbers nor do they stand for numbers; they are marks which stand in place of numerals. By convention, if a pronumeral occurs more than once in a sentence, and one of its occurrences is replaced by a numeral, than all of its occurrences are replaced by that numeral. For example, two conversions of '$x - 5 = 7 - 2x$' are '$8 - 5 = 7 - 2 \cdot 8$' and '$4 - 5 = 7 - 2 \cdot 4$'. The job of *solving an equation* is simply one of finding true conversions of the equation. A number whose name converts an equation into a true sentence is a solution or root of the equation. The equation '$x^2 + 1 = 17$' has the two roots 4 and $-4$ because these are the only numbers whose names convert the equation into a true sentence.

In developing the idea of the pronumeral as a place holder for a numeral it is easy to prepare students for the important job of stating generalizations about numbers. For example, when a student encounters the sentence '$x + 3 = 3 + x$', he guesses quickly that each conversion of this sentence is true because the conversion is an instance of the commutative principle for addition.

(He is aware of the commutative principle for addition, as well as other properties of addition and multiplication, and in our program he has learned the word 'commutative' before he has encountered pronumerals.) In fact, he may even maintain that '$x + 3 = 3 + x$' is "always" true, or that '$x + 3 = 3 + x$' is true for all numbers. What he is saying, of course, is that when any number is added to 3, the same sum is obtained as when 3 is added to it. Although the slight ambiguity in the foregoing sentence is not troublesome, when the student tries to verbalize other generalizations, such as the distributive principle for multiplication over addition, he finds that the ordinary procedure for using pronouns in English does not lend itself readily to precise statements of even moderately complex generalizations. He needs a method of "keying" pronouns, and keying is accomplished by using a *quantifier* phrase such as the prepositional phrase in:

For all numbers $x$, $y$, and $z$, $x \times (y + z) = x \times y + x \times z$.

The displayed sentence is the distributive principle for multiplication over addition. The student must not regard this sentence as a statement about the letters '$x$', '$y$', and '$z$'. Instead, he should regard it as a statement about multiplication and addition of numbers, and should see the statement as being equivalent, in some fashion, to the conjunction of its instances. An instance of this generalization is obtained by taking the sentence which follows the quantifier, selecting a number from the set of *all numbers*, writing a name for it in place of each occurrence of '*x*', and repeating this procedure for '*y*' and '*z*'. Thus, an instance is:

$$9 \times (3 + 7) = 9 \times 3 + 9 \times 7.$$

An illustration of the ease with which a student can state a generalization which he has discovered is provided by an incident which occurred in a class in one of our pilot schools. A student had difficulty in finding the number which when multiplied by 7 would give 5 as the product. After some experimenting, she discovered that 5/7 was the number in question. The teacher then posed a series of questions:

> What multiplied by 7 gives 3?
> What multiplied by 7 gives 9?
> What multiplied by 12 gives 17?
> What multiplied by 0 gives 5?
> What multiplied by 93 gives 88?
> What multiplied by 1087 gives −95?

When rapid answers to questions such as the last were obtained, the teacher was certain that the student was aware of a generalization. He then asked for a statement of the principle the student was using. A good rendering of the generalization in ordinary English might be: the number you multiply by a second number other than 0 to get a third number is the quotient of the third number by the second number. There are very few ninth graders who can use English in such a precise fashion. But there were many students in that class who were able to offer the following statement:

For all numbers $x$ (except 0) and $y$, $x \times \frac{y}{x} = y$.

Although the neologism 'pronumeral' is used in the early part of our beginning course instead of the more usual 'numerical variable', the standard terminology is introduced just as soon as the need arises for the generic term 'variable'. This occurs in the latter part of the ninth grade when the student notices some of the properties of operations with sets. For example, he may observe that in the sentence:

$$x \smile y = y \smile x,$$

the letters hold places for names of sets instead of names of numbers. Although the letters are pronouns, they are not pronumerals. Here we introduce the word 'variable'. (The fact that a word with the connotation of change should be used for this purpose seems strange to our students.)

One can give a defense of the language used in conventional courses by saying that many of the usages are colloquial or elliptical, and that such idiomatic modes of expression are helpful in facilitating informal communication. We grant the importance of using colloquialisms and elisions, but we also insist that students know what is being idiomatized. For example, if a student says that "you can add $3x$ and $5x$", we want him to understand that he means that the distributive and commutative principles can be used to transform the expression '$3x + 5x$' to '$8x$', and that he does not mean that $3x$ and $8x$ can be added because you can add "like numbers". If he says '$\angle ABC = 30°$', we want him to intend this as an abbreviation for 'the degree-measure of $\angle ABC = 30$' or for '$\angle ABC$ belongs to the magnitude $30°$'. He may talk about the line '$3x + 5y - 7 = 0$' but he should understand that he means the line which is the set of all ordered pairs $(x, y)$ such that $3x + 5y - 7 = 0$.

Although the careful use of language in textbook exposition is perhaps more a writer's problem than it is a mathematician's problem, our attempt to be precise has had important consequences for the mathematical content of our program. Here are some examples of these consequences.

Once he is convinced that numerals are not numbers, it is natural for the student to wonder what numbers are. While it is probably too difficult to give a complete answer to this question in secondary school courses, we have given examples of how some number systems are constructed, and we have compared these developments with a postulational approach. The complex-number system is a case in point. In conventional courses, students first learn that there is no number whose square is $-1$, and later are asked to accept the notion that there is such a number. It is certainly more satisfying to students to learn that complex numbers are ordered pairs of real numbers, to learn, next, the definitions of the operations with complex numbers, and to show that the complex-number system is a field, and finally, to derive the theorem that the complex number $(0, 1)$ is a square root of the complex number $(-1, 0)$.

The semantic notion that a noun ought to have a referent has led us to give precise descriptions of relations and functions. The customary vagueness that surrounds the word 'function' in conventional courses vanishes when a student realizes that a function is an entity, a set of ordered pairs in which no two elements have the same first component. The pedagogic advantage of this type of precision is apparent, for example, when the teacher deals with the concept of the inverse of a function. A student who understands that a function is a set of ordered pairs has no trouble in "picturing" the inverse of a function, or in determining whether a function has an inverse. Also, a student who has learned the set-of-ordered-pairs definition for functions does not have the common misconception of conventional students that a function is an equation. Thus, our students are completely at ease with the idea of functions whose domains and ranges do not consist of the same kind of elements. They respond well to the development of the circular functions, cosine and sine, from the notion of a "winding" function. The winding function is a function whose domain is the set of real numbers and whose range is the set of ordered pairs which belong to the unit circle. Although the functions cosine and sine are functions from numbers to numbers, we easily "extend" this idea for purposes of application to functions whose domains are sets of classes of congruent angles, and to functions whose domains are sets of radian-measures of angles or degree-measures of angles.

The fact that our students are aware that nouns should have referents helps them in understanding the role of primitive terms in a postulational system. Primitive terms are nounlike words without referents (and, for this reason, postulates are statements without content). We have found it relatively easy to work with models of a deductive theory because our students understand that one may construct a model by supplying referents for the primitive terms. Also, they have no trouble in understanding the logical role of definitions in a deductive theory because they are familiar with a mode of expression which refers to replacing one string of symbols by another.

DISCOVERY

A second major principle which has guided us in developing the UICSM program is that the student will come to understand mathematics if he plays an active part in developing mathematical ideas and procedures. To us this means that after we have selected a body of subject matter to be learned we must design both exposition and exercises in such a way that the student will discover principles and rules.

It may be argued by some that this procedure is too authoritarian, and that the most desirable situation would be to permit the student to proceed without preselection of content and without direction. We concede that this may be a desirable state of affairs in a class which is under the tutelage of a gifted teacher. But we are developing a curriculum for the mass of schools which demand a preselected content and for the mass of teachers who want textbooks. And we maintain that even with preselected content there are opportunities for the expression of individuality on the part of the student. Some of our most fruitful text developments and revisions have come from problems suggested by our students and from leads which they have uncovered and pursued.

In what follows I present several examples of developments in our program which result in discoveries by students. I do this to illustrate our notion of discovery. The illustration is followed by a defense of the "discovery method" of teaching mathematics.

Teachers of the conventional course in beginning algebra recognize the fact that students are very quick in discovering a rule for adding directed numbers. In fact, the usual rule stated in textbooks is a necessarily complicated description of an algorism, and usually contains some confusion of symbol with referent. Any student capable of learning algebra in the first place will have invented this algorism. Any student who is able to interpret the textbook description is also able to carry out the algorism for adding without using the text description. Hence, our earliest opportunity for an important discovery in the UICSM program occurs in connection with the rule for adding directed numbers. All students succeed in this first attempt. On the other hand, the complete algorism for multiplication is seldom discovered under conventional treatments. Moreover, since we regard the positive numbers as different from the nondirected numbers, our students cannot discover that "$(+4) \times (+3) = +12$ because $(+4) \times (+3) = 4 \times 3$". In fact, since we regard a positive number such as $+4$ as different from the number 4, we were compelled to invent a physical interpretation for symbols such as

'(+4) × (+3)' and '(+4) × (−3)' just as we invented a physical interpretation for symbols such as '(+7) + (−8)' and '(−3) + (−2)'. (Of course, the algorism must eventually be justified either by a definition of the operation in question and a definition of directed numbers, or from postulates for the directed-number system. But, since we feel that neither the constructive nor the postulational approach is appropriate at the eighth- or ninth-grade levels, we make do with a carefully contrived and reasonable physical interpretation.) Once a student accepts the physical interpretation, he can use it to simplify symbols such as '(−4) × (+3)'. He is eager to find a way to get answers without using the physical interpretation. So he hunts for an algorism; when he finds it, he says that he has a short cut. The student who is slow to discover the algorism can continue to use the physical interpretation; the fact that others in the class are getting answers with great speed is usually enough to spur him on toward discovery.

It is important to point out here that it is unnecessary to require a student to verbalize his discovery to determine whether he is aware of a rule. The teacher can use a sequence of questions to determine whether the awareness is present. In fact, immediate verbalization has the obvious disadvantage of giving the game away to other students, as well the more serious disadvantage of compelling the student to make a statement when he may not have the linguistic capacity to do so. This is especially the case when a student does not yet know how to use variables. A premature verbalization is, almost by definition in such a case, imprecise and, thus, not a faithful rendering of what the student actually believes, or is coming to believe. The teacher's acceptance of an imprecise verbalization is a signal to the student that he has completed the process of searching for a generalization. And even a precise verbalization from the student is not a sure sign that he is aware of the class of instances of the generalization, for he may regard the generalization itself as just another "instance". (The preceding sentence is a possible explanation of the phenomenon of the student who has "learned" a rule or has even "discovered" one as evidenced by his stating it, but who misapplies it in subsequent exercises.) This technique [5] of *delaying* the verbalization of important discoveries is characteristic of the UICSM program, and differentiates our discovery method from other methods which are also called 'discovery methods' but which always involve the immediate verbalization of discoveries.

One should not infer from this discussion of delayed verbalization that we believe that verbal-

[5] Gertrude Hendrix, "A New Clue to Transfer of Training", *Elementary School Journal*, XLVIII (December 1947), 197–208.

ization is unimportant in the learning of mathematics. Verbalization is necessary, for example, in the many cases in which a student believes that he has discovered a generalization, and wants to show that it is a theorem.

A second area in which the UICSM curriculum insists upon discovery is that of solving simple equations and inequations. When a student understands what an equation is and what is meant by solving an equation, he is ready to devise his own algorisms for solving equations and inequations such as:

$$x + 3 = 9, \qquad\qquad 3x = 15,$$
$$2(x + 1) - 5(3 - x) = 29, \qquad \frac{5x + 1}{3} = 7,$$
$$|x - 3| = 4, \qquad\qquad |2x + 1| < 7.$$

Many of the teachers working with our program in pilot schools expressed considerable skepticism, at first, about the ability of students to do this without being given the formal algorisms ("doing the same thing to both sides") beforehand. The success of their students was a source of gratifying surprise to them. Students develop considerable facility in solving equations of the type illustrated and are well motivated to learn the formal algorisms when they encounter an equation such as '$3x - 2 = 7 - 5x$' which does not yield to what they call "the common-sense method" but which is much simpler in appearance than many they have already solved.

A third area for invention is that involving rules for manipulating algebraic expressions. Conventional textbooks place great stress on giving step-by-step descriptions of the algorisms for manipulation and simplification. Our contention is that these rules should be invented by students since they are merely short cuts in applying basic principles. Once a student has learned what is meant by 'equivalent expressions' and the basic principles of arithmetic (essentially, the properties of a field), he is ready to simplify expressions in a meaningful way. Consider, as an example, the expression '$3x + 5x$'. After just a very few replacements of the '$x$'s by numerals, the student is ready to conjecture that '$8x$' is equivalent to the given expression. (That it is simpler is, for his purposes, just an aesthetic decision.) Since by 'equivalent' he means that a name of each number of the domain of the variable '$x$' converts the sentence '$3x + 5x = 8x$' into a true one, he cannot verify equivalence of expressions by trying each member of an infinite domain. So he demonstrates the equivalence of the two expressions by deriving the simpler one from the given one as follows:

By the commutative principle for multiplication, for every $x$, $3x + 5x = x3 + x5$. And, by the distributive principle, for every $x$, $x3 + x5 = x(3 + 5)$.

Again, by the commutative principle, for every $x$, $x(3 + 5) = (3 + 5)x$, or $8x$. So, for every $x$, $3x + 5x = 8x$.

Now, I doubt whether there is a ninth grader to whom you would want to teach algebra who would believe that it was *necessary* to go through the preceding demonstration to discover the simpler expression '$8x$'. Our students are urged to invent whatever procedures they can to arrive at simpler expressions as efficiently as possible. The formal derivation from basic principles is used only occasionally, mostly to demonstrate that short cuts are evidences of artistry rather than wizardry. Frequently, students will derive theorems from the basic principles, such theorems being nothing more than precise verbalizations of the short cuts. For example, ninth graders will insist, after two or three demonstrations of the type shown above, that "we prove once and for all that it always works that way". So they formulate and derive the sentence 'For every $x$, $y$, and $z$, $yx + zx = (y + z)x$', invent a name for this generalization such as 'the second distributive principle' or 'the commutative-distributive principle', and refer to this derived principle whenever they use it in demonstrating the equivalence of expressions.

The close ties maintained between the manipulation of expressions and the basic principles do not enable us to eliminate drill in manipulation.

The student needs to practice using his short cuts in order to attain proficiency in their use. But during this practice the student knows that the algorisms he is using have a foundation in the basic principles and are not fortuitous procedures which seem to produce the right answers because the "book said so". Moreover, if a student errs in applying a short cut, for example, in simplifying '$3a + 2b$' to '$5ab$', he is made aware of his error either by a classmate giving a counterexample to the generalization 'For every $a$ and $b$, $3a + 2b = 5ab$', or by the teacher insisting upon a derivation of the generalization from basic principles. (A question such as: How did you get '$5ab$'? is never raised, for the answer is obvious: the student found the sum of 3 and 2, put down a '5', and wrote an '$ab$' next to it.) Whenever possible the routine drill exercises are tied in with activities of greater intrinsic interest which may lead the student into discoveries. Examples: (1) drill in factoring is provided in exercises on solving quadratic equations; (2) practice in computing with directed numbers is provided in exercises on graphing sentences in a one-dimensional space ('$xxx < 0$', '$|3x - 5| \leq 7$', '$- (x - 3)/2$ is a nonnegative whole number'); (3) practice in adding and graphing complex numbers is incorporated in exercises in which the student plots several real multiples of a given complex number, adds a second given complex number to each of the real multiples, and discovers generalizations concerning collinearity; (4) intensive drill in plotting ordered pairs is obtained in carrying out dice-throwing experiments which lead to discoveries of generalizations in elementary probability theory.

A rather striking example of how routine drill can provide students with opportunities for discovering principles which were not included in the text occured in one of our classes. The students had derived the two-point form for obtaining a linear equation where the locus contained two given points, namely: For each two points $(x_0, y_0)$ and $(x_1, y_1)$, $\{(x, y): (y_1 - y_0)(x - x_0) - (x_1 - x_0)(y - y_0) = 0\}$ is the line which contains $(x_0, y_0)$ and $(x_1, y_1)$. As drill, students were given triples of points and asked to determine whether the points were collinear. The "recommended" procedure was to use the two-point form to write an equation of the line determined by two of the points, and then check to see if the third point satisfied the equation. The setting up of the equation and the checking involved a fair amount of tedium, and the teacher soon discovered that the students were testing collinearity by determining whether a pair of first component differences was proportional to the corresponding pair of second component differences. This seemed to be more efficient than using the two-point-form technique, and just about every student in the class had hit upon the proportionality approach. The teacher then raised the question about the connection between the two approaches: Was this just a lucky coincidence, or was the two-point form essentially equivalent to the proportionality between pairs of corresponding differences of components of the points? A less sophisticated class would have been asked merely to think about this question, and not have been expected to give a formal derivation of one technique from the other. But this class was able to give precise descriptions of each technique, and so a formal derivation was in order. The question was answered by the students in considerable detail, and the ensuing discussion resulted in a fairly complete treatment of the notion of slope, including a derivation of the point-slope form for equations of nonvertical lines. The apparently universal tendency of children to reduce complex procedures to less complex and routine ones is a drive which will result in creativeness if the student is encouraged to find the "easy ways".

Somewhat related to the notion of discovery in teaching is our insistence that the student become aware of a concept before a name has been assigned to the concept. (This awareness frequently leads to the student's invention of a name, an activity which also involves creativity.) This point of view has enabled us to include in our program certain concepts which observers claim belong to the province of graduate courses in mathematics because of the "abstract" nature of the concepts. Our experience in teaching students that a relation is a set of ordered pairs is an example. To be sure, we take considerably more time in getting our students to arrive at this notion than can be taken at the graduate course level. (But it may also be the case that the reputation that this notion has of being difficult can be attributed to the fact that not enough time is devoted in graduate courses to building the concept for the student!) Through a series of activities and exercises in which a student becomes quite familiar with graphs of sets of ordered pairs (advancing from finite domains and ranges to infinite ones), the student builds for himself the concept that a set of ordered pairs is an entity and that membership in the set can be expressed by means of a graph, and, in some cases, by means of a simple sentence. Since the sentence also expresses in a vague way a "relation" between the components of a member of the set of ordered pairs, it is natural and convenient to regard the set itself as the relation. By focusing the student's attention on the graphs of relations, it is possible to build considerable geometric intuition about such properties of relations as reflexiveness, irreflexiveness, symmetry, asymmetry, antisymmetry, and transitivity. Our students are comfortable with phrases such as 'equality is a subset of congruence', '$\geq$ is the converse of $\leq$', and 'proportionality is an equivalence relation'. It is an easy step from the general study of relations to the study of functions as a special class of relations.

A criticism of the discovery method runs something like this. It consumes too much time. Since the most important thing you can do for high school students is to help them acquire consummate skill in manipulation so that they can solve lots of problems, it is best to give, by rule and by example and with dispatch, all of the manipulative algorisms. Do this so that the student will have the maximum amount of time available for practice. Occasionally, the teacher should ask a few questions as he derives a formula at the blackboard, but this type of questioning should not be pushed far because the student cannot be expected to know a derivation he has not seen carried out prior to that time. (Since only the brightest can ever reproduce derivations anyway, you can't include them on tests. Also, college entrance examination questions are multiple-choice, so there really is no good reason to waste effort on derivations.)

If the sole or even the major purpose of mathematics instruction in the secondary school were the preparation of students for college entrance examinations and for carrying out the manipulations required in analytic geometry and calculus courses in college, this criticism of the discovery method would be justified. Students with a strong interest in mathematics, particularly in problem solving, have thrived under a "tell 'em and test 'em" kind of regimen. But we know that many high school students, including the more able ones, have been repelled by mathematics courses, and, judging from the criticisms of college teachers, the products of the conventional manipulation-oriented curriculum are not well prepared for college mathematics.

When the manipulative procedures in mathematics are presented as perfected techniques to be learned and practiced by students, it is to be expected that students will inquire into the purpose of such activity. Clearly, there is small need in the life of the high school freshman for a highly developed talent in solving quadratic equations. He may believe you when you tell him that such a talent will "pay off" when he gets to college, but I do not think that he regards this as a valid reason for expending so much effort at the age of fourteen. He may even contrast his mathematics course with the one he is taking in literature. In literature he spends much time in learning things

which make sense in terms of his present existence; in addition to the aesthetic appeal of literature, there is the appeal based on opportunities to
understand himself and his human environment.
I am afraid that the "how-to-do-it" course in
mathematics does not fare well in a comparison
with courses in literature or science. If we want
to develop proficiency in the processes of mathematics (and this is a very important objective),
and if we want students to feel that this activity is
worthy of earnest pursuit, we need to work
toward this end in an indirect manner. We need
to involve students in problems whose solutions
require the use of manipulative processes. But the
problems must make sense to the students, and
the students must be allowed to invent the methods
of solution. These two aspects — sensible problems and opportunities to invent solutions — are
the keys to maintaining interest in mathematics.

Now, a sensible problem for a ninth grader is
not necessarily a sensible problem for an adult.
The child's world is, of course, different from the
adult's. It is rich in fantasy and not at all bounded
by the exigencies of making a living and providing
for old-age security. A child delights in the what-
would-happen-if type of question, and, if he can
give consistent answers to such questions, he regards this work as being eminently practical. If
he is consistently unsuccessful in finding answers

to these questions, they become artificial, uninteresting, and impractical.

Consider a student whose interest has been captured by the game of converting sentences containing variables into true sentences. (There must be sentences like '$|2x - 5| \leq 7$' and '$8 + |5(x - 3) + 4/x| = 3$' as well as like '$x + 4 = 9$' and '$3x = 12$', or else the game loses its challenge.) You can sustain this interest by making him rely completely upon his own resources in playing the game, and you can destroy the interest by telling him all the rules for getting answers. You can make him receptive to developing techniques more formal than the ones he has invented by giving him sentences such as '$5x + 3 = 8 - 2x$' and '$x^2 + 5x = 6$'. The very fact that a student can discover techniques for himself is all the evidence he needs to see mathematics as a human endeavor which demands creative energy.

The discovery method of teaching is practiced by those who believe that mathematics is more than a tool to be used in solving the "real-life" problems of mankind. And the student who is seldom encouraged to discover even the real-life-tool features of mathematics will find himself ill equipped to construct solutions to new problems. Thus, the discovery method develops interest in mathematics, and power in mathematical thinking. Because of the student's independence of rote rules and routines, it also develops versatility in applying mathematics.

### THE EMERGING UICSM PROGRAM

From the time of the initial use of its first textbook in September 1952 at the University of Illinois High School, the UICSM program has been subject to continual revision. We accept the need for revision as a normal concomitant of our work. That there is such a need is not to be wondered at, since we have not hesitated to make radical changes in the content and the development of the traditional program. We are continually apprised of the success of our efforts as a result of our close communication with the classes in our pilot schools. The weekly written reports from participating teachers, the regional training conferences, the results of our testing program, and the detailed reports made by our teacher coordinators, who visit the pilot schools, all serve as sources of information on which to base revisions. Although the final formulation of our syllabi is still to be made, we are now aware of a certain amount of stability in sequence and content. Thus, a description of the present content is in order.

Our program begins by leading the student to an awareness of the distinction between things and their names — in particular, of the distinction between numbers and numerals, and of the need when writing about numerals (or other expressions) to have names for them. He is then told of the existence of real numbers ("directed numbers") as contrasted with the "unsigned" numbers of arithmetic with which he is already familiar. Through the use of real numbers in solving problems he discovers how to add and multiply them, and he discovers that the operations of addition and multiplication have the usual properties of commutativity, associativity, etc. He learns of subtraction and division as inverse operations, and studies order relations and the absolute-value operation. He discovers the usefulness of numerical variables both in connection with the problem of expressing the properties he has discovered of these operations and relations and in the use of equations and inequations in solving "worded" problems. In the former connection, he also learns something of the procedure of deducing a sentence from other sentences; and while solving equations and inequations he becomes aware of the set concept and develops some of the notation (and concepts) of the algebra of sets. Finally, he studies Euclidean plane geometry from an informal point of view. In this development, stress is placed on the notions of measures of intervals, arcs, angles, and plane regions, and the main elementary properties of angles, triangles, quadrilaterals, and circles are discovered either by measurement of figures or by deduction of theorems from previously discovered theorems.

The second year deals, first, with the notion of ordered pair and a study of the solution sets of equations and inequations in two variables. After further development of the algebra of sets, the student arrives at the concept of a relation as a set of ordered pairs, and notices such properties of relations as reflexiveness, transitivity, antisymmetry, and so forth. He discovers the connection between equivalence relations and partitions. He develops the two-point form for linear equations of lines, and the two-point form for parametric equations of lines (incidentally discovering and using the relation of proportionality for ordered pairs of real numbers), and finds methods for studying the intersection properties of number plane lines. Next, he considers those relations which are functions. He discovers that some functions have inverses. As illustrative numerical material, he studies linear and quadratic functions. He now reviews the number system of arithmetic (the "unsigned" real numbers) by accepting certain principles as postulates and deriving others from these. This review forms a basis for a development of the real-number system in which the real numbers are defined to be equivalence classes of ordered pairs of numbers of arithmetic, and the properties of the real numbers as an ordered field are derived from the definitions of the operations of addition, opposition, multiplication, and reciprocation together with the postulated facts concerning the system of numbers of arithmetic. In this development he arrives at the usual algorisms for multiplication and division of polynomials. A discussion of ways in which the numbers of arithmetic can be constructed from simpler number systems leads to the consideration of the natural numbers and the introduction of the principle of mathematical induction. Recursive definitions and proof by mathematical induction are treated at length, and illustrated by the use of $\Sigma$-notation and the theory of arithmetic progressions.

Our third year begins with a study of exponents, in which use is made of recursive definition and proof by mathematical induction, and a study of logarithms as exponents. Here the student begins to develop the concept of continuity and the limit concept; the theory of geometric progressions, and the binomial series come in naturally at this point. Next, the complex-number system is constructed on the basis of the system of real numbers. The procedure is such that the student first learns about the complex numbers as forming a linear vector space and on this basis (linear independence and so forth) makes the familiar applications of complex numbers to geometry. This is followed by a rather detailed process of discovering a suitable definition for multiplication of complex numbers. Finally, the student considers polynomial functions and studies such aspects of the theory of equations as the factor theorem, synthetic division, and curve tracing.

The fourth year contains a treatment of the circular functions based on a winding function. The emphasis is on such properties as periodicity, evenness and oddness, and monotonicity, and on "analytic trigonometry" rather than on "triangle solving", although applications are made to two- and three-dimensional mensuration problems. Solution of equations which involve the circular functions is based on a careful treatment of the inverse circular functions. The work on circular functions is followed by an outline of a purely deductive treatment of Euclidean plane geometry in which the student learns that a deductive theory can be obtained by abstraction of postulates from a model and deduction of theorems from these postulates without reference to the model, and that such a deductive theory can then be reinterpreted to yield information about other models. The remainder of the course is devoted to a study of plane and solid geometry by analytic methods.

CONCLUSION

The UICSM program is a product of the combined efforts of mathematicians and teachers. It is an attempt to determine what the teacher must do to bring to the mind of the adolescent some of the ideas and modes of thinking which are basic in the work of the contemporary mathematician. The success of this attempt is a result of the dedication of our staff and of the participating teachers in the pilot schools, and of the generous support of the University of Illinois and of our foundation sponsor, the Carnegie Corporation of New York.